River Runners

- a tale of protected species

naturally scottish

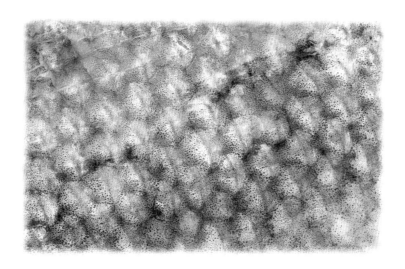

SCOTTISH NATURAL HERITAGE

Acknowledgements:

Author: Iain Sime (SNH)

Series Editor: Lynne Farrell (SNH)

Design and production: SNH Design and Publications

Photographs:
Laurie Campbell P23 top, **Lorne Gill/SNH** Front cover right, frontspeice, PVIII, P12, P13, P15, P21, P23 bottom, back cover top left, **David Hay** P17, P18, P24, P36 top, **P&A Macdonald/SNH** P35, **Alastair MacEwen/OSF** P34, **Brian Morland** P29, P30, P32, **NHPA/Agence Nature** P28, **John Paling/OSF** front cover bottom left, P31, P36 bottom, **Glynn Satterley** P6, P7, P25, **Sue Scott/SNH** Front cover top left, P VII, P8, P10, P11, **Sue Scott** P2, P9, P16, P20, P36 centre

Illustrations:
Kelly Stuart/SNH P5, P19, P27

Scottish Natural Heritage
Design and Publications
Battleby
Redgorton
Perth PH1 3EW
Tel: 01738 444177
Fax: 01738 827411
E-mail: pubs@snh.gov.uk
Web site: http://www.snh.org.uk

Cover photograph:
Freshwater pearl mussel,
Atlantic salmon and River lamprey

Frontspiece: Salmon scales

Back cover photograph:
The River Dee near Braemar

River Runners

- a tale of protected species

naturally scottish

by

Iain Sime (Scottish Natural Heritage)

Foreword

For years the conservation of fish was neglected in Scotland - a surprising fact since there are more fish species than all other vertebrate groups together and since fish are so important commercially. However, with the participation of the United Kingdom in various international conventions - notably the Bern Convension and the EC Habitats Directive - considerable attention is now being paid to our most threatened species.

One of the exceptions to lack of protection is the Atlantic salmon which has had protection for hundreds of years. Yet this species too is in decline. Much of past legislation has been aimed at protecting the fishery and not the fish. This together with new pressures, has meant that only in the last decade or so has action been taken to manage its riverine habitat.

Lampreys, on the other hand, have had no protection until recently. My first contact with brook lampreys was in the River Allander where, in the 1940s, pollution below Milngavie acted as a complete barrier to migratory fish. Thus, there were no river or sea lampreys, Atlantic salmon, sea trout or eels in the stretches near my home. Happily, with recent improvements in water quality, lampreys and other species can now reach the upper Allander.

Aquatic invertebrates too are receiving protection from European legislation. Perhaps Scotland's most amazing invertebrate is the freshwater pearl mussel - what other invertebrate is able to grow to a large size, requires calcium for its heavy shell yet thrives in calcium-poor waters, and can live for over 100 years! Its historical connections add to its importance, for Scottish pearls adorn our Crown as well as Sceptre, last used at the close of Parliament over 300 years ago.

This new conservation interest in salmon, lampreys and mussels is being translated by Scottish Natural Heritage into action to protect rivers in which they occur. The fact that they all require clean, unpolluted rivers means that sustaining them in the future will be a symbol of our success in maintaining high water quality in rivers and lochs - so important for tourism and industry. This booklet is one of the building blocks in raising awareness of our responsibilities towards these animals and, in so doing, moving Scotland to a better future for them and us.

Professor Peter S Maitland
Fish Conservation Centre, Haddington

Contents

Freshwater pearl mussels feeding in a Highland river

River Carie by Loch Rannoch, Perthshire

Introduction

Species of conservation concern

Scotland supports some of the strongest remaining populations in Europe of a number of vulnerable animal species. These include the Atlantic salmon, three species of lamprey (sea, river and brook) and the freshwater pearl mussel. All these are found in Northern Europe and beyond but many have declined to such an extent that Scotland is now considered to be a stronghold for their remaining populations.

The salmon, pearl mussel and lampreys are all linked by a river's complex 'web of life' whereby each can be dependent on another for its continued survival. Very young pearl mussels rely on the presence of young salmon in the river for their survival, and some species of lamprey depend on salmon and other fish species as a food source. In turn, both pearl mussels and young lampreys feed on small particles in the river water, and abundant populations of these species may help to maintain the cleanliness of river systems needed by other animals, including salmon.

Freshwater Pearl Mussel

What is a pearl mussel?

Freshwater pearl mussels are related to many other more familiar marine mussel species such as common mussels and scallops. Pearl mussels are similar in shape to marine mussels but grow much larger and live far longer than their marine relatives. In fact they have a complex and fascinating life cycle during which they can live for well over 100 years, and in that time reach a length of over 15cm. Pearl mussels are dark brown to black in colour and feed by drawing in river water and filtering out fine particles. They live at the bottom of clean, fast-flowing rivers.

Famously, and as their name suggests, freshwater pearl mussels bear pearls which have provided this mussel with an illustrious place in our cultural history. Yet over-exploitation for pearls presents a very serious threat to the continued survival of pearl mussels and pearl fishing is now illegal in Scotland.

Freshwater pearl mussels in a Highland river

Habitat and Distribution

The freshwater pearl mussel has very specialised habitat requirements which are found in many upland rivers in Scotland. Pearl mussels live partially or totally buried in coarse sand or fine gravel, often around boulders and other large rocks that help to stabilise the river bed.

Pearl mussels also require fast-flowing water that is free from pollution. But, despite having a shell that is made from calcium, they are only found in water that is low in this mineral. Hence their original distribution in Scotland reflects that of non-calcareous rock. They were once found throughout Scotland except for the Tweed catchment, parts of the Central belt and the sandstone area of Caithness. But now, due to a number of threats, pearl mussel distribution has been reduced to a few remnant populations in Southern Scotland and some more abundant populations in the Highlands.

Pearl mussels are known to be sensitive to pollution with lower oxygen levels, slight increases in nutrient levels, silt and heavy metals all causing damage. As mussels often live buried in the river bed and require clean flowing water, anything that clogs up the spaces in the sediment can be extremely damaging. This is particularly true for juveniles that most often live entirely buried in the river bed and they can be the most vulnerable to enriched or silty conditions.

In the few populations where pearl mussels are still abundant, it is thought they can play an important role in helping to cleanse the river water. An adult can filter up to 50 litres of water every day and therefore a very large population will help to maintain the high water quality needed by the resident fish species and other animals and plants living in the river.

Reproduction

As pearl mussels often live in fast-flowing rivers and burns there is always a danger that, over time, floods will sweep the population downstream to the sea. To counter this, they have developed a complex and intricate means of reproducing that includes hitching a ride on young salmon or trout in order to recolonise upstream areas. In doing so the overall population is able to remain in the river.

Reproduction begins in the early summer when male pearl mussels release sperm. These are drawn in by females and the fertilised eggs develop into larvae within the females until mid to late summer. The larvae (glochidia) are effectively microscopic mussels (0.06mm long) and are released by the females and swept downstream. Most of the glochidia are swept away and die, for to survive the larvae must be inhaled by a young salmon or trout and attach themselves to the gills. The chances of this happening are extremely low (less than 0.0004%) and therefore each mussel produces vast numbers of larvae, between one and four million.

Those larvae that do manage to become attached to the gills of a salmon or trout remain there and grow for almost a year where they have no harmful effect on the wild fish. Then, the following spring or summer, the larvae drop from the gills and settle onto the river bed.

The young pearl mussels rely on landing on areas of river bed that are suitable habitat. This is fine gravel or coarse sand. If they do land on such areas, they bury themselves in the sediment where they grow for up to 100 years, reaching sexual maturity after 12-15 years.

FRESHWATER PEARL MUSSEL LIFECYCLE

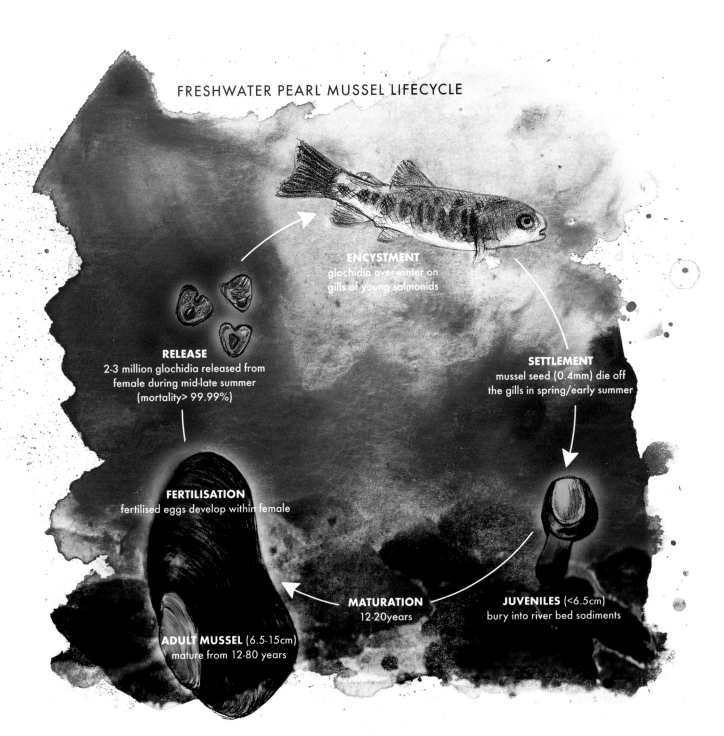

ENCYSTMENT
glochidia overwinter on
gills of young salmonids

RELEASE
2-3 million glochidia released from
female during mid-late summer
(mortality> 99.99%)

SETTLEMENT
mussel seed (0.4mm) die off
the gills in spring/early summer

FERTILISATION
fertilised eggs develop within female

MATURATION
12-20years

JUVENILES (<6.5cm)
bury into river bed sodiments

ADULT MUSSEL (6.5-15cm)
mature from 12-80 years

Pearls

Exploitation of freshwater pearl mussels has taken place since pre-Roman times. The earliest reference to their occurrence in Britain is by Julius Caesar's biographer, Suetonius, who stated that Caeser's admiration of pearls was a reason for inspiring the first Roman invasion in 55BC. In Scotland, the earliest reference dates back to the 12th century when Alexander I, King of Scots, was said to have the best pearl collection of any man living. The medieval poem 'The Parl' which dates from the late 14th century is another early reference to freshwater pearl mussels in Scotland.

There are further references in the 16th and 17th centuries that indicate a growing commercial exploitation of Scottish pearl mussels. At this time the famous Kelly pearl was collected from a tributary of the River Ythan and is thought to be part of the Scottish crown jewels. However, there were soon the first indications that the collection of pearls in Scotland was unsustainable and overfishing was taking place. This followed the arrival in Scotland during 1861 of Moritz Unger, a merchant from Germany. He encouraged the freshwater pearl trade by offering to buy all pearls that could be collected.

Pearl fishing before legal protection of the mussels took place

Pearl fishing kit - note many thousands of mussels would have been killed to yield this amount of pearls

This resulted in many people being employed in the industry but, as too many mussels were collected, it gradually became more difficult to find pearl-bearing mussels and the trade declined.

Since the 19th century there has been a smaller-scale fishery for freshwater pearls, yet dramatic declines in freshwater pearl mussel abundance and distribution have still been recorded over the past 100 years. This decline seems to have accelerated more recently with evidence that pearl mussels have become extinct from an average of two rivers every year in Scotland since 1970. Such declines resulted in full legal protection in 1998.

"As all who search, do by experience try,
And we oftimes; therewith I loudlie cry.

Good master Gall, behold I found a pearle,
A jewel I assure you for an Earle.

Be silent, said good Gall, or speak at leisure,
For men will cut your throat to get your treasure"

The Muses's Threnodie: of Mirthful Mournings on the death of Mr Gall. By Henry Adamson, 1638

Salmon parr and freshwater pearl mussels in a fast-flowing river

Pressures

A recent survey of Scotland which visited rivers known to support pearl mussel populations 100 years ago found that almost two-thirds of populations were extinct or on the verge of extinction. Now there are only 57 populations in Scotland that show signs of reproduction, which represents about half the known remaining world-wide populations. Several of these rivers support abundant populations, but many are in apparent decline. The principal causes of this dramatic decline were identified as pearl fishing and pollution.

Pearl fishing has occurred at virtually every Scottish river and it has been a regular sight to find hundreds to thousands of pearl mussel shells forced open and left on river banks. Easier access to most of the Highlands by road, where the majority of pearl mussel populations remain, has meant that rivers which were previously extremely remote are now accessible and the populations are vulnerable to destructive pearl fishing. It has been estimated that, if the recent rate of decline in pearl mussels continues, there will be no Scottish populations left in 25 years' time.

Water pollution has also been responsible for the early decline in many populations, particularly in lowland areas of Scotland where pearl mussels have now largely disappeared. As pearl mussels are filter feeders and pass considerable amounts of water through their digestive system they are very vulnerable to water pollution. The presence of increased nutrient levels from sources such as agriculture and sewage effluent is a particularly recent problem and several important pearl mussel populations have been lost because of it.

A further threat comes from declines in sea trout and salmon stocks in recent years, which pearl mussels rely on during their first year of life. There is concern that the decline in salmon and trout stocks to historically low levels in several rivers in the North West Highlands could threaten the long-term survival of many pearl mussel populations. Further research is under way to investigate the decline in salmon and trout numbers and the coincident decline in pearl mussel populations.

Silt-laden water from upstream bank reinforcement work

Conservation

Research has begun on how pearl mussels can be artificially reared in order that they can be reintroduced and supplement the existing populations. Reintroduction may help because it is thought that juvenile pearl mussels are particularly vulnerable to disturbance when they are released from the host fish and attempt to settle and grow on the river bed. If it becomes possible to rear pearl mussels artificially then it should also be possible to reintroduce them into rivers that have previously lost their populations due to historically poor water quality and/or pearl fishing.

Work is under way on a number of projects that aim to conserve pearl mussel populations in Scotland. Part of this includes surveying many of the most important populations in detail in order to further our understanding of their distribution, particularly within some of the very large river systems.

Recently our understanding of pearl mussel ecology has increased and this has helped inform how those rivers that continue to support pearl mussels are managed. Applying this knowledge should help to ensure that those populations are able to survive and increase in abundance.

Collecting net for freshwater mussel larvae

Freshwater pearl mussels feeding

Atlantic Salmon

A revered fish

The Atlantic salmon, or 'King of Fish', is both the largest and best known fish that lives in Scotland's rivers. Not only does it have a long relationship with humans and is an extremely important contributor to rural economies, but it also plays an important part in the overall ecology of our rivers. Salmon only breed in clean, pristine waters, and the presence of populations in over 350 of Scotland's river systems is testament to the cleanliness of many of these.

The historical importance of salmon to humans is indicated by the fact that the world's oldest known illustration of a fish is of a salmon, which is in a cave in the Dordogne, France. This dates from 25,000 years ago.

In Scotland salmon were later revered by the Celts and Picts and carvings exist from various locations. The historical legacy of salmon also lives on in place names. The Norse word for salmon was 'lax' and places such as the River Laxford in Sutherland and Laxdale in Lewis reflect the importance of salmon.

Scottish rivers have long contained high-quality salmon populations which have in turn supported world-famous fishing. These populations can produce magnificent fish with the British rod-caught record for salmon being over 29kg on the River Tay in 1922. Despite recent declines in salmon numbers, particularly marked in many west coast rivers, salmon fishing continues to attract thousands of fishermen every year. Another recent development is the importance of fish farming.

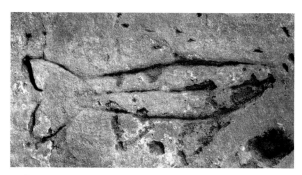

Fish carving on a cave wall at Wemyss, on the Firth of Forth

The Craw Stane, a carved Pictish standing stone near Rhynie, Aberdeenshire

Migration

Part of the reason for the Atlantic salmon's renown is undoubtedly the epic migration it undertakes from the river it grew up in, to distant oceanic feeding grounds, the return to its 'home' river and then on to spawn in the gravel beds of its birth. Salmon from Scottish rivers mainly leave between April and June, when they are called 'smolts'. Once in the sea, they begin an arduous journey to feeding grounds around Greenland and the Faroes. There they feed, along with salmon from North America and Scandinavia, on a diet that includes shrimps, squid, sprats and sand eels.

Salmon remain at sea for an average of one to two years, although some stay longer. Those returning after one year are known as 'grilse'. Losses at sea are high - they are taken by a variety of predators including humans, seals and large fish such as sharks, but sufficient numbers are able to return to the river to produce the next generation.

Little is known about the habits of salmon at sea but in order to complete such an impressive migration and return to the river of their birth, salmon are thought to use several methods of navigation. In the oceans they may use currents; closer to the river mouth chemicals in the water are likely to be important, and when ascending the river further,

chemical and visual information guides them to their spawning grounds.

Salmon in Scottish rivers are unique in that they return from the sea almost all year round. Those that return early in the year tend to have been at sea for more than one year and will be migrating to spawning grounds in the uppermost reaches of their 'home' river. Once back in the river, adult salmon generally do not feed, resulting in a prolonged fast and a loss of 40% of their body weight by the time they spawn. Yet they retain sufficient reserves of strength to ascend waterfalls up to 3m high, and can frequently be seen negotiating these spectacular and seemingly impassable obstacles, such as Rogie Falls on the Black Water and the Falls of Shin, Sutherland, during the summer.

When returning from the sea, both male ('cock') and female ('hen') salmon have silver sides and a silver/white belly, but as spawning time approaches the male in particular will change markedly both its colour and appearance. Such male fish can be known as 'Tartan Fish' due to the mixture of red, brown and purple colours which develop on the sides and back. The male also develops a prominent upturned hook ('kype') on the lower jaw.

Atlantic salmon leaping

Atlantic salmon

The spawning grounds to which the salmon are returning are typically gravel beds in relatively shallow, fast-flowing water. Salmon reach their spawning grounds during October to December when the female will excavate a depression in a gravel bed by lying on her side and repeatedly swishing her tail. This action lifts the gravel and carries it downstream. Then, when the spawning site (or 'redd') is about 15cm deep, she releases her eggs into it and they are immediately fertilised by an accompanying male. The female then fills in the redd, burying the eggs. During spawning the male fish aggressively chases away other fish. The splashing associated with spawning behaviour can sometimes be seen, especially when it happens in very shallow water and the backs of the fish are exposed.

After spawning the male fish remain near the redds in order to mate with any other females; however, they eventually become very weak and die. The majority of female fish also eventually die, but a small proportion are able to migrate back to the sea to feed ('kelts') and survive to spawn again.

Male and female Atlantic salmon

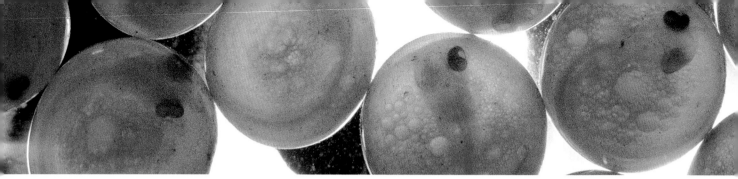

Life in the river

Mature female salmon are extremely fertile fish, depositing thousands of eggs in a redd. The number of eggs each female salmon produces depends on her size at the time of spawning, but a female often produces around 1,100 eggs per kilogram of body weight. The eggs develop in the redd and hatch during March or April. The very young salmon ('alevins') have a large external yolk sac on which they feed for their first few weeks, remaining buried in the gravel until late spring. Then they emerge as young salmon ('fry') and disperse to feed. Salmon fry compete for the best feeding areas with the strongest individuals displacing the weaker ones to poorer feeding areas. During their first year the vast majority of fry will die from starvation and predation.

After one year living in the river 'fry' become 'parr' and they usually remain feeding there for a further one to three years until they are ready to migrate into the sea. Fry and parr feed on a variety of aquatic insects that live in the river, but also feed on other insects that accidentally land on the water surface or fall in from overhanging trees.

As the parr get ready for their passage to the sea they begin moving down the river and become 'smolts'. A number of changes take place as a parr turns into a smolt in preparation for life at sea. The fish becomes more streamlined and silvery in appearance and loses the dark markings along its side. Smolting usually occurs during late spring and soon smolts gradually experience a change from fresh to salt water as they swim out into the estuary. When smolts leave the river they are about 10-20cm in length and once they begin feeding in the sea growth is extremely fast. A salmon smolt that typically weighs about 100g when it leaves the river will, after only one winter at sea, often weigh around 3.5kg.

ATLANTIC SALMON LIFECYCLE

Parr can become smolts in spring and swim down into the sea from April to June

In the sea, salmon migrate huge distances and grow quickly

Parr feed in the river for 2 - 3 years

SEA

On their return to the river salmon stop feeding

RIVER

Alevins hatch in early spring and emerge as fry in May

Spawning takes place in late autumn

Many salmon die after spawning

Atlantic salmon resting under a fallen tree, River Shee

Habitat requirements

Salmon utilise a number of habitats during their life in Scottish rivers. For spawning they require clean gravel beds that allow sufficient water to flow through the gravel and keep the incubating eggs supplied with oxygen. The fry and parr feed over cobbly river beds and shelter behind boulders and submerged debris when resting and to hide from predators.

When the parr begin to smolt and migrate downstream it is essential that there are no barriers preventing them from reaching the sea. The same is also true for adult salmon ascending the river to spawn. Dams and weirs can represent considerable obstacles to migration so many are fitted with fish passes, allowing salmon to pass the barrier by breaking the height difference into a series of manageable steps. At some sites, such as Faskally Dam in Pitlochry, facilities are provided for watching salmon ascending the ladder.

During the upstream migration, adult salmon require deeper pools for shelter and rest. They will also wait in pools for the correct time of year to begin spawning once they are close to their spawning grounds. Pools used by adult salmon can become well known locally as good fishing beats and often have a long history with strange and evocative names such as Carry Wiel, Galoshan and Weetles on the River Tweed.

Fishing

For a very long time salmon have been regarded as a valuable asset in Scotland and the right to fish for them has been closely protected. This right has principally been held by the Crown and large landowners, although it can be held independently of land ownership. The earliest laws regarding salmon date back to the time of King Alexander II (1214-1249). Many further Acts were passed in the 15th century and the value of salmon in those times can be appreciated from the severe punishment meted out for those caught poaching. For example, records show that any poaching at the Ness Islands, Inverness, between 1460 and 1488 was punishable by the poacher being nailed through the ear lobe to a wooden post, known as being 'luggit at the toon'.

Various methods have been used to catch salmon including different kinds of nets on the coasts and estuaries, traps, and (most famously), rod and line fishing in rivers. Fishing by rod and line supports a valuable part of the Scottish tourism industry and remains a major incentive for attracting visitors to the countryside where fishermen can test their skill in catching the 'King of Fish'.

The right to fish at many beats on productive rivers such as the Tweed and Spey are highly sought after and can be leased or sold for immense sums. As recently as 1997 the value of net and rod salmon fishing to the Scottish economy was valued at £450 million per annum.

Fly fishing on the River Findhorn

Pressures

There has been a steady decline in the abundance of salmon in Scottish rivers in recent years. In 1975 the total Scottish salmon catch was about 500,000, but this had decreased to about 100,000 by the year 2000. Much of this decline is due to changes in the fishing methods but there does appear to have been a real and worrying decline in the numbers returning to our rivers, particularly in the smaller and more vulnerable west coast rivers. However, the decline has been far more marked in other countries and Scotland continues to support significant populations. Four countries, including Scotland, together support approximately 90% of the world's healthy Atlantic salmon populations.

Salmon appear to be under threat in both their freshwater and marine phases. In fresh waters the decline in the quality of juvenile and spawning habitat is thought to be having the greatest effect with changing land-use and water pollution often to blame. In the sea the greatest cause for concern is the poor survival rate and the resulting low numbers of returning adults.

Climate change may be affecting salmon through changes in sea surface temperatures which in turn reduce suitable feeding areas around Greenland and the Faroes.

Almost all of the UK - farmed salmon production is located in Scotland. Salmon farming has expanded rapidly since the 1970s and production has risen from 32,000 tonnes in 1990 to 129,000 tonnes in 2000. The presence of farmed fish can threaten wild salmon in several ways, but it is the disease and parasite threat that is of most concern. Farmed fish can harbour sea lice and the highest levels of infestation in wild fish correspond to those areas used for salmon farming. Voluntary Area Management Agreements have been implemented around several parts of the coastline aimed at reducing sea lice infestation in salmon farms and thereby helping local wild salmon and sea trout populations. Escaped farmed salmon are often larger than their wild counterparts, making male farmed fish more attractive to wild female salmon and more successful in spawning. But, the farmed males are not as well adapted to the local environment as wild males resulting in less well-adapted offspring that are less likely to survive and therefore less able to produce the next generation.

Exploitation of adult salmon is difficult to measure, but clearly salmon destined for Scotland and elsewhere are exploited by high seas and coastal fisheries. There is evidence that significant numbers of juvenile salmon are captured as part of the 'by-catch' for commercial marine fisheries.

Sea lice on salmon

Salmon farm, Shetland

Conservation

In response to the recent declines in salmon catches many fishing proprietors have encouraged fishermen to adopt 'catch and release' practices to increase the chance of the adult fish being able to spawn. In many such schemes all caught fish are returned to the river. Several coastal and river netting operations have also been closed in recent years in order to lessen the exploitation of salmon. Closure of coastal netting is particularly important as it often takes salmon indiscriminately from a range of different rivers.

Continuing improvements to water quality have also benefited the salmon, and led to their return to rivers from which they have been absent for many years due to pollution. For example, salmon have naturally returned to the River Clyde in recent years after being absent for more than a century.

Where rivers have suffered serious declines in salmon numbers' programmes to restock the rivers have been put in place in order to help population levels recover. The rivers are restocked with salmon fry grown from eggs that are removed from some of the returning females which were captured the previous year. The adult fish are 'stripped' of their eggs, fertilised with milt extracted from wild male fish, and incubated artificially. This yields a greater survival rate than would otherwise be found in the wild and the integrity of the local population is maintained.

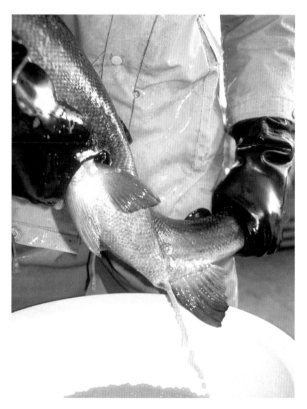

Stripping eggs from a female Atlantic salmon

24

Releasing salmon into the River Carron

Lampreys

What are lampreys?

Lampreys must be amongst the most rarely seen and poorly understood of all the fish species found in Scottish rivers. Their fossil remains show that they were around long before the dinosaurs and many familiar plant groups. There are three species of lampreys in Scotland: the brook, river and sea lamprey. They all belong to a group of animals called 'Agnatha' (meaning 'without jaws') which is the most primitive group of all living vertebrate animals. As the name suggests, lampreys lack jaws and instead have very primitive mouthparts surrounded by a large flexible lip that acts as a sucker. This curious feature provides the scientific name for the lamprey family, Petromyzonidae, which literally translates as 'stone suckers'.

Lampreys resemble eels but have several unusual features not seen in most other fish. Instead of bones, they have a skeleton of cartilage. Lampreys also lack scales, and have a single nostril located on the top of the head in front of the eyes. They do not have gill covers but do have a series of seven sac-like gills which open directly through holes on each side of the head. All lampreys have a long, cylindrical body, like that of eels.

The sea lamprey is by far the largest of the three species with adults reaching a length of one meter and weighing up to 2.5kg. Adult sea lampreys are a brownish-grey colour with extensive black mottling, but close to breeding time their colour lightens to a golden brown. The river and brook lampreys, which are closely related to one another, are far smaller. They are both similar in colour, with adults having a dark olive or brown back and a lighter, silvery belly. The river lamprey is intermediate in size between the other two species with adults usually measuring around 30cm and weighing about 60g. Brook lampreys are the smallest with adults only attaining a length of 15cm, yet there are even smaller dwarf populations with adults from one such population on the Isle of Skye often measuring less than 10cm.

THIS DIAGRAM ILLUSTRATES WHEN SOME OF THE MAJOR FISH GROUPS EVOLVED (WITH EXAMPLES)

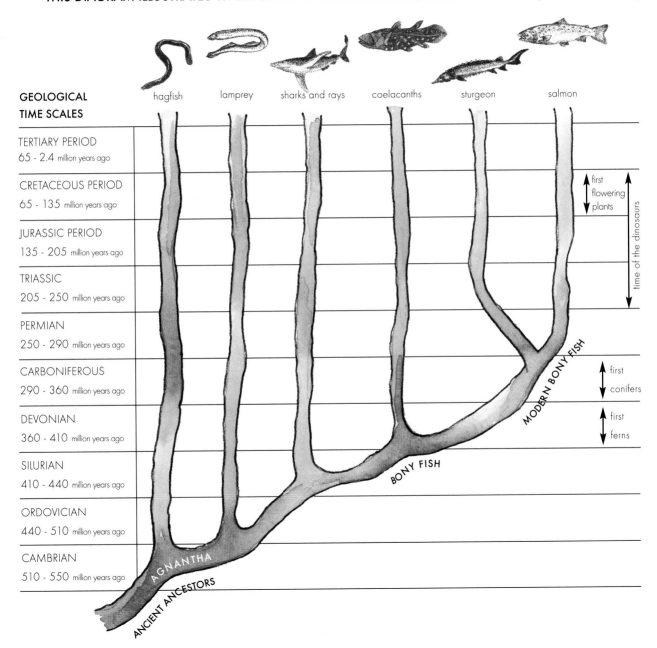

Habitat

More so than any other fish species in Scottish rivers lampreys have two starkly different stages in their life cycle and each stage requires very different kinds of habitat. All three lamprey species have a similar life cycle with the adults migrating upstream to spawn in a depression in gravel beds, in pairs or a group. After the eggs hatch, the blind juvenile lampreys (known as ammocoetes) migrate downstream to silty, slower-flowing parts of the river where, in contrast to the free-swimming adults, they live in burrows until adulthood. Once the ammocoetes become adults they leave the silt beds, eventually returning to spawn.

Two of the three lamprey species - the river and sea lamprey - migrate to the sea as adults, requiring migration routes to and from the sea that are free from barriers such as impassable waterfalls, dams and weirs. All lamprey species are relatively poor swimmers and they are unable to pass obstacles that may be passable to other, faster-swimming species such as salmon or trout. All lamprey species are very sensitive to pollution and require good water quality at all stages of their life cycle.

Breeding

Lampreys are very rarely seen in our rivers as they have extremely reclusive and secretive habits. They remain hidden during all of their juvenile life, living in burrows within silt beds. After they emerge from their burrows as adults they are then largely nocturnal, undertaking their migrations at night. The best time to see them is at breeding time when they seem to throw off their otherwise reclusive habits.

When breeding the adults excavate a spawning pit in a gravel bed by moving stones with their sucker-like mouth. The size of stones that are moved varies, depending on the size and strength of each species. Sea lampreys are able to excavate the largest spawning pits, and it is not unknown for salmon fishermen wading in the river to stumble over them.

River and brook lampreys tend to breed during the spring (March to April), whereas sea lampreys breed in late spring and early summer (May to June). Several adult lampreys can breed together and breeding may extend over several days. The adults seem oblivious to human disturbance, and often spawn during the day in open areas of the river. This makes them vulnerable to predators such as herons, gulls and mink.

The fertility of lampreys varies with the smallest species, the brook lamprey, producing an average of around 1,500 eggs. In contrast, a far larger sea lamprey can produce more than 170,000 eggs. The eggs are small, white and deposited in the spawning pit where they stick to the stones. The eggs typically incubate for less then a month before hatching, and the emerging juveniles then swim or drift downstream to find suitable silt beds for burrowing.

River lamprey over its spawning pit

Feeding

The two different life stages of lampreys feed on very different food supplies. Ammocoetes live in tunnels in the silt and, as their teeth are not yet developed, they feed on small organic particles and algae drawn from the silt surrounding their burrow into their gut in a string of slimy mucus.

All three species spend up to five or more years growing in their burrows before transforming into adults and developing eyes and teeth. One of the differences between the species is that adult brook lampreys do not feed and as such develop very primitive, vestigial teeth. Instead of travelling to the sea they migrate straight to their breeding grounds, mate and then die. In contrast, adult river and sea lampreys swim downstream through July to September to feed in the sea with well-developed, hard, sharp teeth. The arrangement of teeth in the mouth differs between species - in sea lampreys they are arranged in concentric rows with several large teeth also on the tongue, and in river lampreys there are far fewer teeth, all found close to the mouth opening, and on the tongue.

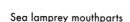

Sea lamprey mouthparts

River and sea lampreys feed on a number of fish species including herring, flounder, sprat, salmon and haddock. They attach themselves to the side of the victim using their sucker-like mouth and attack the fish by rasping away the scales and feeding on the fluids and tissues underneath. Salmon and sea trout that have returned to rivers can sometimes be found with scars from lamprey attacks. The victim may not survive such attacks if the lamprey is able to penetrate the body cavity. Yet despite this parasitic lifestyle there is no evidence that lampreys have a significant impact on any fishery in Scotland.

River lamprey feeding on a trout

River lampreys feed and grow primarily in the estuary, whereas sea lampreys will venture out into the open sea where they have been recorded feeding on cetaceans and sharks. There are also historical records of sea lampreys attaching themselves to the underside of fishing boats, on which they were presumably resting, but they were assumed to have an appetite for tar with which the boats were coated. Very little is known of the behaviour of river and sea lampreys during their marine phase, but it would appear that sea lampreys can travel considerable distances from land with one caught 350km from Ireland in the North Atlantic.

Scotland provides an unusual exception to these normal feeding patterns. River and sea lampreys that breed in the Endrick Water migrate downstream into Loch Lomond and, instead of continuing downstream to the Firth of Clyde, remain in the loch to feed on the resident fish population. This is the only example of freshwater feeding in the UK and one of only three examples in Europe. In Loch Lomond the river lampreys are primarily parasites on trout and the rare powan.

When river and sea lampreys return to the rivers to breed they stop feeding and, like salmon, rely on food reserves to sustain them on their considerable upstream migration.

Wriggling brook lampreys caught during a fisheries survey

History

Lampreys appear never to have supported a fishery in Scotland but have been commonly eaten in various European countries where they are considered a delicacy. Sea lampreys are still eaten in Portugal, and river lampreys, smoked or soaked in oil, in Scandanavia. Lampreys used to be eaten in Scotland, and in 1304 lampreys were imported from France to supply the king while staying at St Andrews. Remains of lamprey teeth dating from the 15th Century have also been recovered from the site of the Cistercian abbey cloister at Dundrennan, near Kirkcudbright.

Lampreys were once highly prized in England and both the Severn and Thames supported substantial lamprey fisheries at one time. Peculiarly, many of the lampreys from these rivers were not fished for food but were exported to Holland as bait for cod and turbot. Most famously the city of Gloucester annually presented a lamprey pie to the reigning sovereign, and it was a surfeit of such lampreys that reputedly killed King Henry I and King John. The kings' deaths were most likely caused by failing to carefully prepare the lampreys before cooking, leading to toxic poisoning.

Although few lampreys are found north of the Great Glen there are several different Gaelic names for lampreys; buarach na baoibhe *(bowruch na byva)*, creathall *(cre-hall)*, easgann bhreac *(acecan vraechd)*, langar leach *(lang-ar eelach)*, naid *(naj)*, rochuaid *(roch-oo-atch)*.

The number of Gaelic names perhaps indicates that lampreys used to be better known to our predecessors than they are to us. Buarach na baoibhe is the most evocative of all the names. Buarach literally means a 'cow-fetter', which is a shackle bound round the hind legs of a cow when milked, and is probably a reference to the cow-fetter's eel-like shape. Baoibhe has various meanings including a she-spirit believed to haunt rivers, and refers to the myth that lampreys were eels possessing magical powers.

Outside of Europe, lampreys are found in North America. There they play an important part in the native culture with the seven gill openings on each side of a lamprey's head said to be the result of lampreys using their bodies as flutes to win an ancient music competition between all beings in the universe, excluding humans.

Female brook lamprey slightly swollen with eggs

Conservation

Scotland represents the northern extent of lamprey distribution in Europe, with few populations found north of the Great Glen. This is thought to be due to the cold temperatures in more northerly rivers which restrict or prevent breeding. Scottish populations are therefore important in maintaining the natural range of the three species both within the UK and Europe.

Lampreys are vulnerable to several threats of which the most potent is thought to be water pollution. There are many rivers in lowland Scotland from which lamprey populations have declined or disappeared, probably as a result of historical increases in pollution from industrial expansion, as well as changes in land use. Their sensitivity to pollution was demonstrated in the River Clyde where, following improvements to water quality,

salmon returned long before river lampreys. However, lamprey ecology is still relatively poorly understood and more research is needed to further our understanding of the fascinating species that inhabit our rivers.

Juvenile lamprey are unusual in living in silt beds, parts of the river that are not commonly used by any other fish species. Therefore this habitat is often not considered in river management and can be vulnerable to activities that fail to take account of the presence of lampreys. Lampreys have also been targeted for use as bait, particularly by pike fishermen. Two tonnes of lampreys are removed annually from the River Ouse in Yorkshire for this purpose - indiscriminate removal of adults for bait can pose a threat to populations and is therefore discouraged.

Species and the law

In response to the vulnerability across Europe of all the species in this booklet important sites have been identified in Scotland and designated as Special Areas of Conservation under the EC Habitats Directive.

Freshwater pearl mussels are also fully protected under the Wildlife and Countryside Act 1981, making it an offence to deliberately kill, injure or disturb them.

Loch Lomond and the Endrick Water

The future

It is hoped that the increased protection all the species have received in recent years will contribute to their continued survival and reversal in fortunes in years to come. Many organisations are working towards securing and enhancing the status of pearl mussels, Atlantic salmon and lamprey species. The designation of Special Areas of Conservation will focus efforts on maintaining the most important populations throughout Europe and lessons that are learned within these sites will be disseminated around, and outwith, the EU.

Within the UK the critically endangered freshwater pearl mussel is the subject of a Biodiversity Action Plan that is working towards increasing their numbers and range in Scotland. Salmon, lampreys and pearl mussels are also the subject of local Biodiversity Action Plans which target actions on local populations throughout Scotland.

It is vital that pearl mussels, lampreys and salmon all continue to survive and prosper again in our rivers as they are all important indicators of general river quality, support a long and illustrious cultural heritage and, as has been illustrated, have important and fascinating roles to play in river ecology.

Atlantic salmon parr

Freshwater pearl mussel feeding

River lamprey ammocoete

Further reading

Mills, D. 1989. *Ecology and Management of Atlantic Salmon.* Chapman and Hall, London.

Maitland, P.S. and Campbell, R.N. 1992. *Freshwater Fishes of the British Isles.* HarperCollins, London.

Cosgrove, P. Hastie, L. and Young, M. 2000. Freshwater Pearl Mussels in Peril, '*British Wildlife*'. Volume 11, pages 340-347.

Maitland, P.S. 2000. *Guide to Freshwater Fish of Britain and Europe.* Hamlyn, London.

Jones, M. 2002. Lamprey: relic from the past, '*Brittish Wildlife,*' Volume 13, pages 381-388.

Cosgrove, P. Young, M. Hastie, L. Gaywood, M. and Boon, P. 2000. The status of the freshwater pearl mussel Margaritifera margaritifera Linn in Scotland, *Aquatic Conservation: Marine and Freshwater Ecosystems'.* Volume 10, pages 197-208.

Also in the Naturally Scottish series...

If you have enjoyed River Runners why not find out more about Scotland's wildlife in our Naturally Scottish series. Each booklet looks at one or more of Scotland's native species. The clear and informative text is illustrated with exceptional photographs by top wildlife photographers, showing the species in their native habitats and illustrating their relationships with man. They also provide information on conservation and the law.

Red Squirrels

The red squirrel is one Scotland's most endearing mammals. This booklet provides an insight into their ecology and some of the problems facing red squirrels in Scotland today.
Peter Lurz & Mairi Cooper
ISBN 1 85397 298 4 pbk 20pp £3.00

Badgers

With its distinctive black and white striped face and short, squat body, the badger is probably one of the most popular mammals in Britain. Packed with stunning photographs, this publication reveals some amazing facts about the shy, secretive badger.
Mairi Cooper & John Ralston
ISBN 1 85397 254 1 pbk 16pp £3.00

Burnet Moths

Unlike many other species of moth, burnet moths fly by day. They can be easily recognised by their beautiful, glossy black wings with crimson spots. Their striking colouring is a very real warning to predators.
Mark Young
ISBN 1 85397 209 6 pbk 24pp £3.00

Sea Eagles

This magnificent bird, with its wing span of over 2m is the largest bird of prey in Britain. In 1916 they became extinct, but a reintroduction programme began in 1975. This booklet documents the return of this truly majestic eagle. Production subsidised by Anheuser-Busch.
Greg Mudge, Kevin Duffy, Kate Thompson & John Love
ISBN 1 85397 208 8 pbk 16pp £1.50

Seals

All around the coasts of Scotland grey and common seals can be found basking on the rocks, resting between fishing expeditions. Gain an insight into how seals live, their amazing grace and elegance in water contrasted to their clumsiness on land, and where and when you can watch seals in Scotland.
Elizabeth Cruwys and John Baxter
ISBN 1 85397 233 9 pbk 24pp £3.00

Corncrakes

Secretive, skulking, rasping, loud, tuneless, scarce. . . all these words have been used to describe the corncrake. But once you could have added plentiful and widespread to the list. Now only a few birds visit Scotland each year. This booklet brings you the latest information on the corncrake and reveals this elusive and noisy bird in its grassy home.
Rhys Green and Helen Riley
ISBN 1 85397 049 2 pbk 40pp £3.95

Red Kites

This graceful and distinctive bird was absent from Scotland's skies for more than a century. Now, with the help of a successful programme of re-introduction, its russet plumage and forked tail can once again be seen in Scotland.
David Minns and Doug Gilbert
ISBN 1 85397 210 X pbk 24pp £4.95

Fungi

Fungi belong to one of the most varied, useful and ancient kingdoms in the natural world. Scotland may have almost 2000 larger species with some of the most interesting found in our woodlands and grasslands. This booklet provides an introduction to their life cycles, habitats and conservation. Discover the fascinating forms of earthstars, truffles and waxcaps.
Roy Watling MBE and Stephen Ward
ISBN 1 85397 341 6 pbk 40pp £4.95

SNH Publications Order Form:

Naturally Scottish Series

Title	Price	Quantity
Badgers	£3.00	....
Burnet Moths	£3.00	....
Corncrakes	£3.95	....
Red Squirrels	£3.00	....
Red Kites	£3.95	....
Sea Eagles	£1.50	....
Seals	£3.00	....
Fungi	£4.95	....

Postage and packing: free of charge in the UK, a standard charge of £2.95 will be applied to all orders from the European Union. Elsewhere a standard charge of £5.50 will be applied for postage.

Please complete in BLOCK CAPITALS

Name _____

Address _____

_____

_____

_____ Post Code

Type of Credit Card VISA ☐   MasterCard ☐

Name of card holder _____

Card Number

☐☐☐☐ ☐☐☐☐ ☐☐☐☐ ☐☐☐☐

Expiry Date ☐☐ ☐☐

Send order and cheque made payable to Scottish Natural Heritage to:

Scottish Natural Heritage. Design and Publications, Battleby, Redgorton, Perth PH1 3EW

pubs@redgore.demon.co.uk

www.snh.org.uk

Please add my name to the mailing list for the: SNH Magazine ☐

Publications Catalogue ☐